Maisy's Colours

Lucy Cousins

WALKER BOOKS
AND SUBSIDIARIES
LONDON · BOSTON · SYDNEY · AUCKLAND

pink whiskers
pink ears
pink hands
pink tail
pink feet

orange
lolly

blue dolphin in a blue sea

brown
horse

green

train

red coat

red carpet

yellow
sand

purple
rocking-horse

black
spots

white
dressing
gown

What
colours
can
Maisy
see?

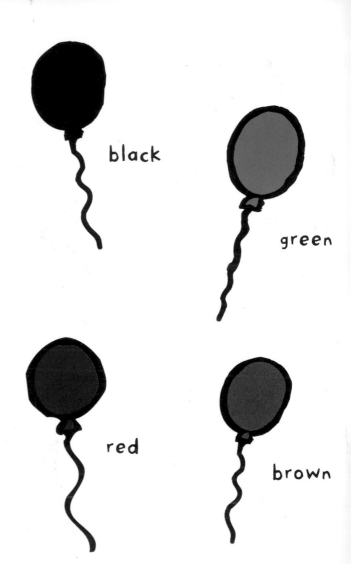

black

green

red

brown

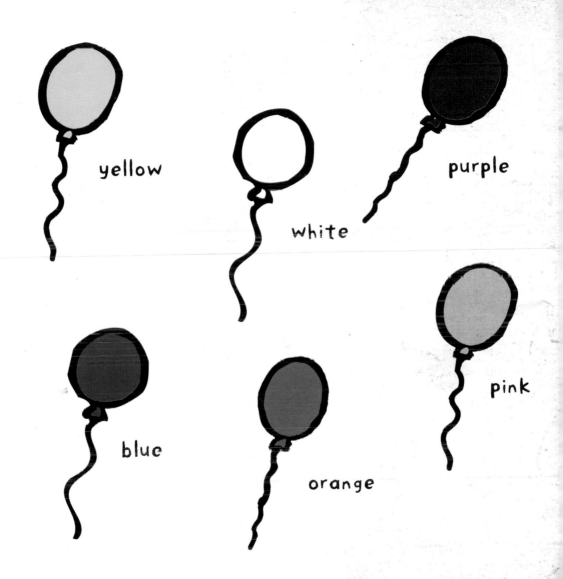

yellow

white

purple

blue

orange

pink

For Rufus

First published by Walker Books Ltd
87 Vauxhall Walk, London SE11 5HJ
in *Maisy goes to the Playground* (1992),
Maisy goes to Playschool (1992) and *Maisy's ABC* (1994)

First published as *Maisy's Colours* 1997

2 4 6 8 10 9 7 5 3 1

Text © 1997 Lucy Cousins
Illustrations © 1992, 1994 Lucy Cousins
Lucy Cousins font © 2003 Lucy Cousins
Maisy™. Maisy is a registered trademark of Walker Books Ltd, London

Printed in China

British Library Cataloguing in Publication Data:
a catalogue record for this book is available
from the British Library

ISBN 0-7445-8665-8

www.walkerbooks.co.uk